There Were Ten in the Bed

For my friend Linda
— S.C.C.

ISBN 0-439-56147-7

Text copyright © 2003 by Scholastic Inc.
Illustrations copyright © 2003 by Susan Chapman Calitri.
All rights reserved. Published by Scholastic Inc.
SCHOLASTIC, SING AND READ STORYBOOK, and associated logos
are trademarks and/or registered trademarks of Scholastic Inc.

12 11   8/0
Printed in the U.S.A.
First Scholastic printing, September 2003

There Were Ten in the Bed

Illustrated by Susan Chapman Calitri

SCHOLASTIC INC.
New York   Toronto   London   Auckland   Sydney
Mexico City   New Delhi   Hong Kong   Buenos Aires

There were ten in the bed
And the little one said,
"Roll over, roll over."

So they all rolled over
And one fell out.

There were nine in the bed
And the little one said,
"Roll over, roll over."

So they all rolled over
And one fell out.

There were eight in the bed
And the little one said,
"Roll over, roll over."

So they all rolled over
And one fell out.

There were seven in the bed
And the little one said,
"Roll over, roll over."

So they all rolled over
And one fell out.

There were six in the bed
And the little one said,
"Roll over, roll over."

So they all rolled over
And one fell out.

There were five in the bed
And the little one said,
"Roll over, roll over."

So they all rolled over
And one fell out.

There were four in the bed
And the little one said,
"Roll over, roll over."

So they all rolled over
And one fell out.

There were three in the bed
And the little one said,
"Roll over, roll over."

So they all rolled over
And one fell out.

There were two in the bed
And the little one said,
"Roll over, roll over."

So they all rolled over
And one fell out.

There was one in the be
And the little one said,
"I FOUND IT!"

There Were Ten in the Bed

1. There were ten in the bed and the lit-tle one

said, "Roll o - ver, roll o - ver." So they

all rolled o - ver and one fell out.

2. There were nine in the bed ...
(verses 3-9—count one less each repetition)

10. There was one in the bed and the
little one said, "I found it!"